Quakers in stitches

Anne Wynn-Wilson

The Quaker Tapestry:
a community embroidery
for story telling and
celebration

The Quaker Tapestry at Kendal Ltd
Friends Meeting House, Stramongate
Kendal, Cumbria, LA9 4BH

Index

3   **Introduction**

4   **The Quaker Tapestry**
       a celebration of creativity and insights

4   Why do we use the word tapestry?

5   How the Quaker Tapestry began

9   **How the Quaker Tapestry was made**

9   Embroidery teaching

11   The research and design of the panels

12   **Style and technique**

12   Unity

12   Stitches

12   Three layers of embroidery

13   Transposing designs

13   Perspective

15   Materials

16   **Making a sampler**

16   Transferring designs

17   The use of a ring frame

18   **The stitches used**

18   Stem stitch

19   Stem stitch used for transposing designs

20   Split stitch

21   Knot stitch or Peking knot

22   Quaker stitch

24   Chain stitch

26   Bayeux point

27   **Embroidered lettering**

31   **Good practice**

INTRODUCTION

A child once said 'something has to happen so something can happen'. That something was the making of the Quaker Tapestry which provided opportunities for workshops, holidays, exhibitions, publishing, television programmes and above all learning new skills and enjoying good friendship.

When a panel of the tapestry has been finished the workers often confide that they didn't think that it could be achieved. But together they have created something beautiful which communicates more than the story line. Their caring and goal of excellence has given the embroidery a life of its own.

The embroidery of the Quaker Tapestry has been shared with Friends in ten countries; the children's drawings were collected from twelve countries. It is estimated that about 300 embroiderers have made it possible for over 4,000 people in 15 countries to participate in making the 77 panels.

A list of the 15 countries involved:

Australia & Tasmania
Britain
Canada
Chile
Eire
France
East Germany
Japan

Mexico
The Netherlands
New Zealand
South Africa
Sweden
Switzerland
United States of America

THE QUAKER TAPESTRY
a celebration of creativity and insights

Since the dawn of recorded history, craftspeople have used their skills to tell stories. Such a record is the Quaker Tapestry – a series of 77 separate crewel-embroidered panels, each measuring 25" (635mm) wide by 21" (533mm) deep, and thus small enough to be easily transported and exhibited. The Tapestry is not an academic history, but a celebration of Quakers' experience and insights as they endeavour to find God's will in everyday life: it is an experiment in education and communication.

The subjects of the panels have been suggested by individual members and adopted by groups for research and embroidery. The vision and enthusiasm sprang from the grass roots; it was not directed as for a commissioned work. The Quaker Tapestry uses a new embroidery style and technique which enables both skilled and unskilled workers to co-operate.

The inspiration for the Quaker Tapestry was the 11th century Bayeux Tapestry, commissioned by Bishop Odo to honour his half-brother, William the Conqueror, by illustrating the story of his conquest of England in 1066. Both embroideries are outstanding examples of story-telling through craftsmanship.

Why do we use the word tapestry?

The Quaker Tapestry is a narrative crewel work, or in other words a hanging which tells a story, similar to the Bayeux Tapestry. Crewel embroidery has appeared in many styles since the ninth century. It is traditionally worked on a twill weave linen. Perhaps the best known designs are based on the Tree of Life, they are often called Jacobean embroidery. The word 'crewel' comes from the ancient word describing the curl in the staple of the wool, the staple being the single hair of the wool. Crewel wool has a long staple, which is fine and can be strongly twisted, and crewel embroidery takes its name from the use of this wool.

The crewel technique is designed to dance freely across the surface

ELIZABETH FRY 1780 1845
Lord·I believe··help thou my unbelief
By her inspiration devotion+charm she attracted public support for her concern to lighten the suffering+ humiliation of women prisoners.

The cartoon (or design) for 'Elizabeth Fry' (panel E5).
See also page 10 for an enlarged detail.
Designed by Joe McCrum. Embroidered by Hilda Jenks
and members of Bournville Preparative Meeting.

of the fabric, quite distinct from canvas work which uses wool for stitches that are regulated by the weave of the canvas. Canvas work is sometimes known by the misnomer 'tapestry work'. In a true tapestry the design is woven directly into the warp threads, using the special technique of tapestry weaving. It is interesting to note that, historically, all three methods have been used to make hangings that tell a story. The French word for a worker in these techniques is tapissière. No wonder there is confusion in naming these textiles!

How the Quaker Tapestry began

On the first Sunday in January 1981 I began teaching a boy in the Quaker meeting in Taunton.

My intention was that we should make a long scroll illustrated with stories from Quaker history. Jonathan, then aged 11, knowing

The cartoon for 'Quaker Marriage' (panel C8).
Designed by Joe McCrum. Embroidered by Ann Castle and members of Bournemouth and Swanage Meetings.

that I was an embroiderer, asked, 'Can we do it in embroidery?'. The Bayeux Tapestry flashed across my mind and I promised to think about it. Jonathan had dropped the pebble into the pool and the rings are still increasing. His seemingly impossible request could become reality if the work was shared by many people.

At that time I sensed within the Society pockets of loneliness, especially amongst the elderly, and a lack of knowledge about Quaker experience amongst the newcomers and the children. Because the tapestry had not been commissioned, I was free to base the project on people, their needs and well-being. This consideration led to many of the unique facets of the Quaker Tapestry Scheme. Embroidery was the catalyst which opened opportunities for an unusual experiment in education, communication and community experience.

From the beginning it was planned that there would be a large number of panels, 60 initially, too many for any one group to achieve on their own. I wanted to give people opportunities, to see a problem and work out how to solve it, and to encourage sharing and interdependence. So it was very important to create a style and technique that could be enjoyed by both the experienced embroiderers and by the young or unskilled. The organisation was to be open for all who wished to join in.

During the first twenty months the fabric was woven and the embroidery style and technique established. The embroidery project with the Taunton children flourished and the class grew from one boy to four boys and a girl and several visiting children. Two newcomers and a few members of the meeting joined the group. The children enjoyed the story-telling and acting. They made exciting drawings and careful embroideries. In all they contributed to nine panels: together we tested the new embroidery style and technique. Some influential Friends thought the project was a 'notion' and not in keeping with Quaker traditions, in fact a waste of time and money. After much prayerful thought, it became clear that the way forward was to organise an exhibition during the Yearly Meeting to be held at Warwick University in August 1982. This would demonstrate the opportunities offered by the project to the large number of Friends who would be present.

I was granted the use of a large classroom for a week. The exhibition was well prepared with a slide/tape presentation showing what had been achieved so far. Two embroidered panels, another ready for demonstration and several cartoons (designs) for further panels were displayed. A manual of stitches and techniques and leaflets describing the project were available. During the exhibition a large group of supporters was gathered and the first Quaker Tapestry Scheme Committee formed. Without this shared responsibility the work could not have made any progress.

Many people offered subjects for selection and joined the research work. Friends suggested 404 subjects that might be included in the Tapestry: 60 were finally selected by the new committee and offered for adoption by individuals or Quaker groups: a further 17 panels have been accepted since 1982. The adoption of subjects brought responsibilities. Each group undertook the research, but not design work. They agreed to complete the embroidery in the accepted style

Cartoon for 'Reconciliation' (panel F9).
Designed by Anne Wynn-Wilson.
Embroidered by members of Belfast meeting.

and colour. All embroidery materials were supplied free, on the understanding that money for the project would be raised by the adopting group according to their size and ability to support the scheme financially. Throughout the making, the embroiderers were encouraged to use the opportunity to share information and friendship, especially with the children and attenders at meetings. The project was an example of 'inreach' not 'outreach': a wider interest from the public was not recognized until later.

HOW THE QUAKER TAPESTRY WAS MADE

The larger groups had a leader and were linked to an embroidery adviser. The groups were expected to honour their agreements about style and technique but their members retained their freedom to organise the work for the convenience and enjoyment of themselves. Each embroidery group had its own personality. The membership varied in size and so did the geographical area they covered. The Scottish panels travelled from Newton Stewart to Orkney and reached a wider public on television, others travelled across continents, whilst some stayed in one place. Everyone was welcome; men, women and children, especially non-Quaker spouses.

Embroidery teaching

Embroidery was taught in three types of workshop and a manual was available for the embroiderers.

1. Residential weekend workshops were held at Woodbrooke (the Quaker college in Birmingham) or in one of the Quaker guest houses or study centres
2. One day workshops were usually held in a meeting house
3. Small workshops were held in homes.

The group leaders and many of the embroiderers attended these workshops and then shared their knowledge with others.

Residential weekends became a notable part of the Tapestry Scheme. Our secretary, Margaret Simpson, looked after bookings, money and welfare. By popular request we ventured into Tapestry Holidays. The most notable one was at Charbonnières, a Quaker château in Normandy, where 68 Friends enjoyed a Holiday Workshop. Our subject was 'Story-telling through the crafts'. Our programme included visits to Chartres Cathedral, to the Cluny Museum in Paris and to Bayeux to see the Bayeux Tapestry. We took

our embroideries to show to the curator at Bayeux and were over-joyed when we received an invitation to exhibit the Quaker Tapestry in Bayeux in 1990.

The research and design of the panels

Some embroidery groups enjoyed research, others were grateful for help from a central research team. It is essential to agree the essence of the story and select quotations before the design begins. Cartoons were accepted from fourteen artists and many drawings from children in twelve countries. But our main designers were Joe McCrum, Margery Levy, Wendy Gillett and myself. As co-ordinator my aim was unity throughout, but to allow the artists' individuality to remain in both the design and creative embroidery.

The cartoon for the embroidery design was prepared as a full scale drawing complete with headings and lettering. Photocopies were made and individual stitch instructions and colour notes added (see left). This instruction sheet travelled with the embroidery frame to the makers who were encouraged to date and sign the sheet. If they wished they could add embroidery advice and comment. The New Zealand cartoon returned with 273 signatures! Surely a proof of 'one-stitch' well wishers as well as dedicated embroiderers.

Left detail of the cartoon for 'Elizabeth Fry' (panel E5)
showing detailed instructions for the embroidery.
*Designed by Joe McCrum. Embroidered by Hilda Jenks
and members of Bournville Preparative Meeting.*

11

STYLE & TECHNIQUE

Unity

The unity of the tapestry depends on details common to all seventy-seven panels. An important feature of all crewel work is the use of crewel wool and the importance of the background fabric. All the panels are the same size and each is divided by a pair of golden brown lines into three sections. The lettering follows an agreed design and spacing and is embroidered in a rusty red colour throughout.

The following conventions were adopted: faces and hands, in line only; clothes, fully embroidered; buildings, doors, windows and roofs, solid embroidery; walls, in outline; animals, trees, furniture and detail, in creative descriptive embroidery.

Style (how it looks) and technique (how it is achieved) in embroidery are very closely related. The distinctive style of the Quaker Tapestry depends on the use of six stitches and three layers of embroidery.

Stitches

Four traditional stitches	stem stitch (page 18)
	split stitch (page 20)
	Peking knot (page 21)
	chain stitch (page 24)
One ancient technique	Bayeux point (page 26)
One new stitch	Quaker stitch (page 22)

Three layers of embroidery

The Quaker Tapestry Technique uses three layers of embroidery

The first layer of embroidery is the stem stitch transposed outline. Parts of this may remain untouched as in the face or hands. If part of a line needs emphasising, build it up by whipping.

The second layer of embroidery provides the plain area of colour and texture. The shape may be embroidered in Bayeux point or many

12

lines of one of the stitches. According to the direction of the stitches and their smoothness there will be a difference in the light reflected. Attention to the order of the work can creat overlapping edges which describe depth or layers, e.g. a shirt overlapped by a coat. These points play their part in creating three-dimensional effects.

The third layer is the descriptive creative layer. The stitches move freely over both the plain shapes and the background fabric.

The Quaker Tapestry style and technique was designed to include and encourage everyone who wished to join in the making, whatever their previous embroidery experience. The creative embroidery and the lettering satisfied the experienced workers whilst the simplified use of stitches made it possible to include children and those who had never undertaken any embroidery before without sacrificing the high quality of craftsmanship.

Transposing designs

To overcome the problem of transposing a complicated design on to a rough woollen fabric, a trapunto quilting technique is used. This is a most unusual and successful way of transferring an embroidery design (page 19). The neat line of stitches becomes an integral part of the design, especially in capital letters where the outline provides the structure to hold the decorative Quaker Stitch.

Perspective

Most embroidery designs are considered to be two-dimensional. Narrative crewel work uses the interplay of the three layers of embroidery with colour, tone, texture and contrast to produce the illusion of depth.

Be aware:

Strong hot colours and contrasts come forward.
Rough textures, detail and outline also appear to come forward.
Blues and muted colours recede, as do simple shapes.

Complicated groups of people with a background design can be

Detail of 'Firbank Fell: George Fox Preaching' (panel B1).
Designed and embroidered by Anne Wynn-Wilson.

resolved into three 'back-drops', as in a theatre set. Use the most positive colour and details for the nearest people. For the second line, harmonious colour and very little creative embroidery. For the third, background design, neutral tones and little texture or contrast.

Materials

The woollen fabric used for the Quaker Tapestry embroideries was especially woven in Somerset. The colour is based on the local sandstone. Nine different shades were identified and selected to be woven using a random warp to produce a low-key stripe. The stripe and the weave provide a guide to keep the line of lettering and buildings vertical. The woollen fabric was mounted on a calico backing to stabilise the tension.

A woollen fabric was chosen in preference to the traditional linen twill because it is more comfortable to work with and it doesn't show needlemarks after unpicking. The needle marks on the Bayeux Tapestry are still there after 900 years.

Appleton's Crewel Wool was chosen for the embroidery: 120 harmonious colours were selected. Each panel uses about 40 different colours and when the panels are displayed together the colour flows and melds confirming the unity of the embroideries.

MAKING A SAMPLER

You will need:
   Embroidery ring frame, 300mm (12") diameter
   Woollen fabric, 14" square, i.e. 2" larger than the ring frame
   Calico, 14" square
   Selection of crewel wools and needles
   An outline design
   A textile transfer pencil
   Greaseproof paper (modern tracing paper blisters with heat)
   The use of an iron, scissors, ruler and tacking threads

Transferring designs

Work on an ironing board if possible

1. Check that the fabrics are cut on the warp and weft threads. Iron both on the wrong side only. Mark right side 'RS'.
2. Mark the central point, 'CP', of the design on the design sheet, then draw one vertical and one horizontal line through this CP.
3. Position the design on the embroidery fabric checking that the weave is vertical: mark the CP of the design and outer points of the guide lines. Tack these lines precisely, following the weave.
4. Fold the greaseproof paper into quarters and crease. Place the paper over the design sheet, matching CP and guidelines. Trace the design carefully using the transfer pencil. Mark right side 'RS'.
5. Fold the calico into quarters and iron, mark the RS. Match CP and guidelines. Pin securely through to the ironing board.
6. Test the heat of the iron and press the wax traced line on to the calico. Lift the corner of the paper. If the design is not clear, repeat.
7. Place the wrong sides of the calico and embroidery fabric together. Match guidelines, tack together along lines and outer edges. Fix in a 12" ring frame. If a small piece of expensive fabric is used, fix the calico in the frame first, then attach the embroidery fabric using straight tacking across the cut edges.

N.B. The transferred wax line may fade within several months. The permanent outline is brought through, or transposed, from the calico to the embroidery fabric by using stem stitch which appears as a positive design line of neat stitches (see page 19).

The use of a ring frame

Ring frames consist of two rings or hoops of wood, metal or plastic, used for stretching small pieces of work. The two rings fit together, keeping the fabric taut between them. The outer ring may be fitted with a screw. The inner ring can be bound with tape to give a firmer grip on the embroidery fabric.

1. Place the smaller ring flat on the table, cover with the fabrics, right side up.
2. Loosen the screw.
3. Place the larger ring over the smaller one, and press it down all round. If there is a screw, partially tighten it.
4. Turn the frame over placing your finger and thumb on the inner ring to keep it from jumping out; gently pull the fabric taut but don't distort the weave
5. Tighten the screw.

A convenient way to use a frame without a stand is to place the ring so that it protrudes over the edge of a table. Hold the frame in place with a heavy book or in a clamp. This will allow the use of both hands to control the thread (this is a great advantage – do try it).

THE STITCHES USED

Stem stitch

Stem stitch is a very ancient and universal stitch, used in basket making before embroidery was invented. It has appeared in crewel embroidery since the fifth century and consequently is sometimes know as crewel stitch. It produces a compact line which can be whipped if the line needs more prominence.

Method of working stem stitch

Use your needle vertically – hold it like a dart and when working stem stitch on a curve shorten the stitch to achieve a neat rolling stitch and prevent it from becoming 'spiky'. Hold the thread to the outside of the curve before taking the next stitch.

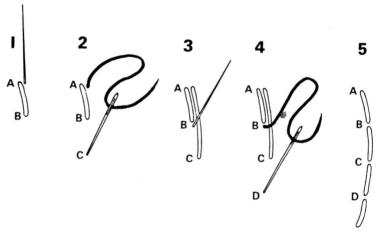

1. To begin, bring the thread up from the underside. Take a small back-stitch and return to the point of entry
2. Continue by bringing the needle up at A and down at C
3. Needle up at B; exactly halfway between A and C
4. Proceed; needle down at D and continue
5. On the reverse side, the stem stitches should appear as a connected line of regular straight stitches. This can only happen if you have used a vertical needle!

18

Stem stitch used for transposing designs

The neat line of straight stitches is used to transpose the design line from the calico backing to the top surface embroidery fabric. This technique for transferring designs is unusual in embroidery but well known as part of trapunto quilting: it is invaluable for the transfer of complicated narrative designs.

Special note. When transposing the design from the calico side to the embroidery fabric work the line on the calico side. Begin with the knot on the calico side, take one stitch forward before beginning the stem stitch. Remember to use a vertical needle.

The neat line of straight stitches which appear on the reverse side of stem-stitch provide a clear guide for future work. Corners in designs, especially in lettering, have to be approached with care; the needle must pierce the exact point of the corner.

The stem stitch transposed line is useful in many ways.

1. Different coloured lines serve as a guide to the colour of infilling. Also, as the outline is being worked the embroiderer should consider which colour will overlap another, eg a white shirt overlapped by a dark coat or a foreground figure overlapping a background horse. These overlays should be noted in the colour of the transposed line: using the correct overlap contributes to the three-dimensional effect.

2. The stem stitch line will pad and neaten all outer edges. If an inner edge needs to visually come forward, put an extra padding of chain stitch or split stitch along the overlapping edge.

When many flowing lines of stem stitch are worked in the same direction they create a smooth, light-reflecting infill. Adjacent lines worked in opposite directions create an interesting rough texture which appears darker in colour than the smooth surface. This technique can be used creatively to produce a three-dimensional effect.

These last points are for the more advanced embroiderer but use them as soon as you feel able to.

See also 'Making a sampler', page 16

Split stitch

Split stitch provides one of the finest lines in embroidery. It was used in medieval embroideries for fine detail, especially hands, faces and flowing silk robes.

A small split stitch is useful for stockings, cuffs and collars. It can also be used on a large scale – a line of extended stitches, of up to 25mm, placed against a reverse row of long stitches, produces a texture which could represent a modern concrete building! Also split stitch worked with four strands of wool looks remarkably like a large chain stitch. Always shorten the stitch when embroidering a curve.

Method of working split stitch

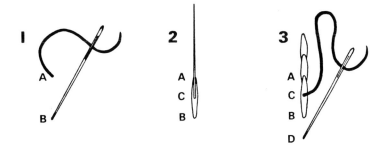

1. Bring the needle up at A and down at B
2. Needle up at C, piercing through the thread from below
3. The needle goes down at D

Knot stitch or Peking knot

As used in Chinese Embroidery

To make a shapely knot, the thread should be twisted around the needle only once. The size of the knot is determined by the number of threads and the size of the needle. The embroidery fabric should be tightly held in a frame which should be clamped or weighted on a table. Both hands must be free to control the thread.

Knot stitch is versatile. It may be used as a seeded filling or a rough nobbly texture. Single knots may represent a full stop, an eye, a button or fine lace, or be used as solid filling for curly hair. Small knots can form flowers, large knots hedgerows. It is a question of density. Well made knots will always lie in the same direction.

Method of working knot stitch

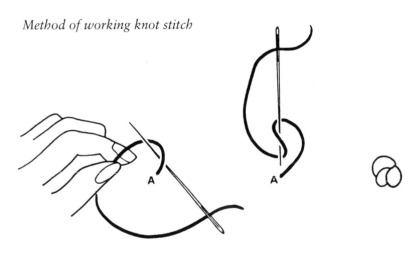

1. Bring the needle up at A
2. With the left hand hold the thread about two inches from the fabric. Twist the needlepoint to pick up one circle of thread.
3. Then place the point of the needle close to point A. Pull the thread closely around the needle; put your finger on the twist of wool as you push the needle down through the fabric. This will ensure that it slides into the right place.

Quaker stitch

Quaker stitch was created by the author to achieve neat, clear lettering on the Quaker Tapestry.

Quaker stitch is compact and corded; it is made by combining stem stitch and split stitch. When worked with four or six threads, it produces a very satisfactory cord suitable for the core of an upper case letter. Worked with one thread, it produces a fine flexible line with no stray ends. Quaker stitch overcomes a problem produced by stem stitch as seen in the lettering of the Bayeux Tapestry.

For practice use a woollen fabric where the threads or fine check can be counted. Mount the fabric and calico backing in a ring frame. Use four threads of crewel wool and a large crewel needle. Put a weight on one side of the frame or clamp it to the table so that both your hands are free to control the thread.

Consider that the full stitch covers nine threads and that it is built up in thirds.

Method of working Quaker stitch

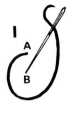 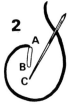  

1. Take a back-stitch over six threads; i.e. needle up at A and down at B, return up again at A. Keep the wool thrown to the left to enable the left hand fingers to control it, keep an even easy tension.

2. Take a full-length stitch over nine threads, needle entering at C. Put your finger on the loop; keep the wool to one side until the needle has returned at D where it splits the first stitch A-B halfway. Draw the

thread through and let the stitch roll into place.

3. Progress three threads, needle down at E. Continue working nine threads forward, as if it were stem stitch and six threads back as if it were split stitch. Don't flatten the stitches by pulling the wool too tightly. Let the embroidery wool stand like a cord.

4. To finish the roll, take a short stitch following the same angle over the last long stitch.

After making the first back-stitch, roll the needle between your finger and thumb rolling away from yourself, this will help to combine the threads and form the cord. When working vertical lines throw the wool to the left and work towards yourself.

Important: on a curve, work in an anti-clockwise direction, always throwing the thread to the outside of the curve.

Left-hand workers need to reverse every move, including working clockwise.

Quaker stitch should not be confined just to lettering, it is particularly useful when embroidering buildings or boat construction.

Chain stitch

Chain stitch is one of the oldest and most versatile stitches. It forms an interlocking flat chain and can be adapted for a large number of variations.

Method of working chain stitch

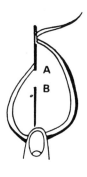 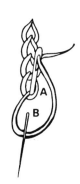

1. Bring the needle up at A.
2. Form a loop, and put the needle down at A again, holding the loop with your finger. Then come up at B directly below A. Draw the thread gently through, forming the first chain stitch.
3. Repeat this stitch, always inserting the needle exactly where the thread came out inside the last loop.

Detached chain stitch (also known as lazy daisy stitch)

Make a single chain stitch and hold it in place with a small stitch. Worked in a half-drop pattern, this stitch can represent building construction.

Whipped chain stitch

First work a row of chain stitches. Then using a tapestry needle or the eye end of your needle, slide the needle under each chain without pulling the thread too tightly. The finished effect should be like a raised cord.

Open chain stitch or fly stitch

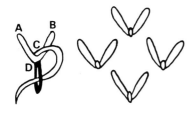

Method of working
1. Needle up at A and down at B
2. Come up at C and catch the thread down at D

Open chain stitch worked in a random way suggests plant life.

Stitches placed methodically make patterns useful for building.

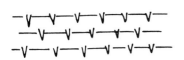

An open chain stitch can be used as a couching stitch or worked over an already couched thread.

Stitches worked in fine thread can represent collars and lace edgings.

Bayeux point

This method of laying threads has gained its name from the Bayeux Tapestry. Bayeux point is the dominant technique used in this embroidery which was commissioned by Bishop Odo and made in Canterbury, England about 1075.

In Bayeux point the majority of the wool remains on the surface, so it is a very economical and suitable technique for decorative work.

Bayeaux Point consists of a foundation of straight stitches, laid either vertically or horizontally, which are tied down with a couched thread placed at right angles. The direction of the couched thread will be dominant when the work is finished. A block with vertically placed couched threads will look darker in colour and more dominant than one with horizontally placed couched threads because the horizontal threads reflect more top light and therefore look paler. This characteristic is very helpful when embroidering adjacent walls of a building or areas of a jacket.

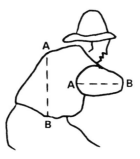

The use of a small set square or the marked edge of a postcard aid keeping lines straight and well-spaced. Different textures can be achieved by changing the spacing of the couched lines. Extra neat edges can be achieved by first working an outline of split stitch, which pads the edge of the area to be filled. Precision is possible if you work stitches with a vertical needle. Neatest edges are where the needle goes down first, not up!

In the Quaker Tapestry technique all the Bayeux point stitches should be worked in the same colour within a single shape.

Stage one

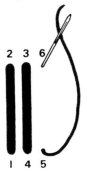

Always use a frame when working Bayeux point. Lay foundation threads vertically or horizontally, evenly across the area to be covered, leaving the width of one thread between each stitch. The first stitch will act as a guide for the others. It should be placed carefully across the centre of the shape. Aim to get an even generous covering of wool; a thin covering tends to split when the couching is done.

Bring the thread up at 1, down at 2 – up at 3, down at 4 until the area is covered.

Stage two

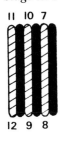

Place one stitch between each pair of stitches already laid. If the first stage is not as even as it should be, it is now possible to correct the situation by inserting more than one stitch where necessary.

Stage three

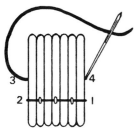

The long thread is placed across the area at right angles to the foundation threads. Tie down the long thread with a small couching stitch placed directly across it. Build a pattern like bricks in a wall. It is helpful to split a foundation thread with the small stitch, so that the foundation threads do not become divided or grouped into bundles. More control is gained if each long stitch is tied down before placing the next long stitch.

EMBROIDERED LETTERING

- The quality of the lettering depends on the care that is spent on detail.

- There are no short-cuts – the correct way is the simplest and quickest.

- The use of an embroidery frame is essential.

It is most important to align the embroidery fabric, the backing fabric and the traced pattern precisely. Even if the vertical transferred line of a letter does not lie on the straight weave of the fabric, the embroidery should always follow the weave.

The design of the lettering is based on 5mm squared paper. Establish the area of the lettering by tacking with bright thread the 15mm height of the letters. It may be useful to use two different colours for alternate lines. Tighten the tension of the fabric whilst you work on detail, and release it when the work is put away.

The lower case letters are constructed directly on the embroidery fabric. For guidance use the vertical weave for vertical lines, and a french curve for a standard oval. **The space between letters** has to be judged but is approximately 1½ squares between straight letters and 1 square between curved letters (see diagram opposite). **The space between words** is the width of one letter, approximately 3 - 4 squares. The design is marked on the backing fabric for guidance, and should be used to establish the beginning and end of each word.

Keep an equal weight in the embroidery line. Use a short thread; after three letters the thread will be wearing thin, which will affect the general appearance of the lettering. Take particular care to begin and finish lines in such a way that the thickness of the stitch is not altered – the letter 't' is particularly vulnerable, especially the cross-stroke. Remember to throw the thread to the outside of the curve when embroidering curved letters and always work Quaker stitch on the straight or in an anti-clockwise curve.

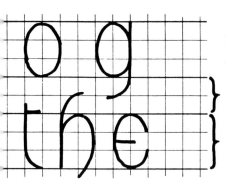

HEIGHT of letters

The space between the lines of lettering is

10mm (2 squares)

The height of the letters is
15mm (3 squares)

WIDTH of letters varies according to their shape

5mm (1 square) wide

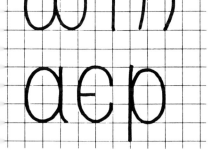

7.5mm (1½ squares) wide

17.5mm (3½ squares) wide

10mm (2 squares) wide
and other letters not shown

The outline of the *upper case letters* (inside front cover) is transposed from the pattern on the backing fabric to the embroidery fabric by the Trapunto quilting technique, i.e. the negative or reverse shape is stem-stitched on the back so that the letter appears on the front as a positive outline of straight stitches (pay particular attention to corners). All small letter embroidery is worked from the front. The core of each large letter is built up in either chain stitch or Quaker stitch worked with four threads. If the letter is very large the Quaker stitch may be outlined with fine chain stitch, using one thread only. This will give a sculptured look to the finished letter.

GOOD PRACTICE

Crewelwork technique: to place stitches precisely the embroidery should be in a frame and both hands should be free to control the thread and needle. Keep the needle vertical and use it as if it were a dart. Ring frames should be clamped to the edge of a table or weighted (see page 17).

Protect the ironing board cover with paper or extra cloth before ironing the wax design on to the calico backing.

No marks should be put on the embroidery fabric except with a quilting pencil. This is a water-soluble marker, not a transfer pencil.

Never iron the embroidery.

Always release the tension on the fabric when work is not in progress otherwise the design will become distorted.

Keep work covered when not in use.

Finished sections can be protected with squares of fabric. When rolling a panel, insert an extra piece of thin material to prevent a line forming.

Skeins of wool can be kept neat and intact by placing a ring of adhesive tape over the name and number band. To avoid pulling the 'wrong end' of the wool, it should be caught under sticky tape. This will keep the band in place, preserve the reference number and avoid tangles.

Text designed and typeset by Jeremy Greenwood
in collaboration with Anne Wynn-Wilson who designed
the cover and embroidered the sampler for it

Tapestry cartoons
© 1995 Quaker Tapestry Scheme
Text and other illustrations
© 1995 Anne Wynn-Wilson

Printed by
Warwick Printing Company Limited
Caswell Road, Leamington Spa, Warwickshire CV31 1QD

Published 1995 by
The Quaker Tapestry at Kendal Ltd
Friends Meeting House, Stramongate
Kendal, Cumbria LA9 4BH

ISBN 0 9525433 0 3